More than Numbers
Everyday Financial Therapy
Participant Workbook

FINANCIAL THERAPY CENTER, LLC

Thomas E. Smith
Victoria M. Shelton
Kristin V. Richards

Southeastern Professional Books, LLC

Books and Guides by the Financial Therapy Center

Financial Therapy: 5 Steps Toward Financial Freedom
Guide to Financial Therapy Forms and Handouts: 5 Steps Toward Financial Freedom

Published by Southeastern Professional Books, Seattle, WA 98116.
www.financialtherapycenter.com

ISBN: 978-0-9883929-2-2

Printed in the United States of America

Library of Congress Control Number 2014914345

TABLE OF CONTENTS

Instructions on the Use of This Guide

This guide contains the handouts and forms that complement the ideas and activities in *More than Numbers: Everyday Financial Therapy Facilitator's Guide.* The handouts and worksheets are meant to stimulate your thinking about personal finances, and attitudes and beliefs about finances. Along with explanations of activities and examples, you will find blank worksheets and spaces included in the manual. These allow you space to write notes and answer questions from the worksheets.

Although the information given in these handouts and worksheets are helpful, it is important that you do not overwork yourself when learning how to improve your finances. Much like the rabbit and the turtle, the only mistake is to start too fast and get overwhelmed. DO NOT, we repeat, DO NOT take on too much. Just like we caution you to be careful about how you spend your money, we also urge you to be careful about how you spend your time while making your way through this workbook. If it's starting to become overwhelming, it's time to slow down.

Your financial therapist will be a mixture of a cheerleader and personal trainer. We are asking you to change your financial lifestyle. It is possible for you to make that change by yourself. However, it will be a lot easier if you have a cheerleader and personal trainer keeping you on track. When learning to manage your finances, any step forward is progress.

Ready? Set? Go Slow!

The Five Steps

Financial therapy consists of five steps that help you identify issues with finances. They are 1) Identify WANTS, 2) Identify NEEDS, 3) Identify what you HAVE, 4) Identify what to DO, and 5) Make PLANS to keep you going, and get back up when you are feeling defeated.

These five steps of financial therapy follow the Stages of Change (Prochaska, Norcross & DiClemente, 1994)[1]. The Stages of Change help people identify how likely they are to make changes, and how to move from one stage to the next. They five stages are 1) precontemplative, 2) contemplative, 3) preparation, 4) action, and 5) maintenance. The interventions in this manual are meant to help you move from one stage to the next by identifying what you want, what you need, what you have, what you're going to do, and what plans you can make for your future.

The first step, "WANT", addresses your desires. This step takes place when you are in the precontemplative stage of change. This means that you are starting to think about how financial therapy might be an important step for you. This step is meant to help you establish overall goals and prioritize your wants.

The second step, addressing "NEEDS", also begins in the precontemplative stage and leads individuals into the contemplative stage. In this step, a discussion of wants is put aside and life is examined in terms of necessity. You'll have to decide what is truly necessary in your life. This is a difficult process, because there is always a difference between wants and needs. In this stage, you'll also identify some things that may have affected your own financial behaviors.

The third stage starts the preparation stage. It signifies a decision to earnestly begin change efforts. During this stage, you investigate what financial resources exist. The HAVE step asks you to examine your current financial situation and not just

---

[1] Prochaska, J. Norcross, J. & DiClemente, C. (1994). *Changing for good: The revolutionary program that explains the six stages of change and teaches you how to free yourself from bad habits.* New York: William Morrow & Co.

your ideal or desired state. You may go through a range of reactions to your current financial state. Frustration, disappointment, and worry are all common. The activities in this manual, along with the interventions presented by your therapist, will help you manage these reactions and put your feelings to good use.

As you enter the fourth step, the action stage of change, it becomes necessary to address what you will do. The "DO" step examines changes you are making, both successful and unsuccessful. In this step, you determine what works best. In addition, you learn to live within a budget that is based on your desires, needs, and aspirations.

The final step, "PLAN" represents a launch into personal financial management. This step focuses on the sustainability of a newly developed lifestyle. You will learn how to recover from financial emergencies that occur when a budget is not followed. Because such deviations can have financial and emotional consequences, you'll learn how to rebound from such losses. Rebounding requires planning. Thus, a major focus in this step is to plan for present and future events. Because financial therapy is designed to be time-limited, planning for the future requires finding continued guidance and education. The final part of this step is to give a send-off after developing a sense of financial self-efficacy. It is not meant to give long-term financial strategies, but instead helps you understand your relationship with money and develop a functional, healthy financial lifestyle.

Step One: Want

Objectives
- ❖ Understand the strengths and limitations of financial therapy
- ❖ Explain the precontemplative stage of readiness
- ❖ Explain the purpose of overall financial goal-setting
- ❖ Prioritize a list of desired services, items and/or activities in terms of pure wants or desires

Step One Rationale
Step One (Session One) helps you identify your financial wants. Financial therapy focuses on changing lifestyles. It addresses emotional and interpersonal reactions to financial problems. The concept of a readiness for change is presented in Step One provides a guidepost on the length of therapy. Step One orients you to the Five Step Financial Therapy model and presents its strengths and limitations.

Session One

Materials Provided
- ❖ Precontemplative Stage of Readiness Handout
- ❖ Setting Personal Finance Goals Worksheet
- ❖ Wants Financial Prioritization Worksheet

Purpose of Session One

Session One describes the strengths and limitations of financial therapy, and will help you become oriented to its purpose. In this session, you will engage in two critical areas of personal finance: 1) writing goals and 2) prioritizing financial wants.

Precontemplative Stage of Readiness Handout

Beginnings in financial therapy don't immediately start with people being in a room. It's okay to start with a skeptical attitude in which problems are minimized or even denied. Let's look at both sides. When faced with financial turmoil, denying its existence creates stress with friends, families, marriages, and with creditors. However, nothing is so hidden as an obvious problem. In short, although you may be experiencing misery, it doesn't mean that you've got to accept everything that we say.

To start, let's agree that change is needed for something to happen, but there will be no demand that it occurs right now. It's a funny thing that change occurs only when there is no other option. We're not going to push you to change your life; there may be a need, but we're not going to judge you and say that you must change now. That just doesn't make sense. It's your life and what you do is your decision.

Everyone is different in how and when they choose to change. What's obvious for some people isn't so obvious for other people. In fact, not moving forward may show caution and respect for "what works right now." However, how will you know when you're ready to make a change in how you manage your personal finances? Remember, in the end, you're in charge of what happens in your life.

Setting Personal Finance Goals Worksheet

For right now, only think about what you really, really want. When push comes to shove, what do you want your financial life to look like? To know what you want, you first must visualize it.

For a moment, think ahead of when you'll have reached your personal finance goals. Think of yourself as having accomplished the goals that you set down today. It's best to be relaxed when you think through the answers to each of the following questions. There is no right or wrong answer. Just relax, and let yourself imagine.

Write your answers to the following questions in the space provided.

   1. What will you be doing when you have accomplished your goals?

   2. Who will be with you?

   3. Where will you be?

4. What will you think about your personal finances?

5. Now that you have imagined your life when your goals are reached, write down your goals:

Who knows best what you want? Well, that would be you. Setting goals is pretty much the same thing. Try to decide what you want. Some people may say "financial freedom", other people may say that they want to plan for their retirement. Financial therapy is not designed to help people become rich or plan for their retirement. So, if those are your personal finance goals, then financial therapy will be a disappointment.

What financial therapy can do is to get you started toward other financial goals. It gets you going on the right path, especially as it concerns your behavior, and your financial relationship with friends and families.

Having said all that, goal setting is not helpful if there's not some dreaming going on. Financial dreams may just be getting out of debt, or it may be to own a bigger house and a newer car. It may be a dream to pay off thousands and thousands in debt and escape the disapproval of friends, families, and stalking by creditors.

Did you know that many sweepstakes winners end up even poorer than they were before they won millions of dollars? A goal within financial therapy is to help people change their attitude toward reducing debt and increasing their assets. It's almost always true: If you change the attitude, that'll change the behavior. Change financial behavior and you'll change your financial status. Okay, now the hard part. What can realistically get done in the next couple of months? The next set of questions will help you answer that tough question.

Circle a number on the scale and write a description in the space provided.

6. On a scale of 1 to 10 (1 being the worst, 10 being the best) rate the current state of your personal finances. Then describe your current financial state.

7. What number do you want to reach by the end of financial therapy? What does that look like?

8. What will you be doing when financial therapy is successful?

Wants Financial Prioritization Worksheet

Goals and wants can seem like the same thing. After all, you *want* to accomplish your *goals*. With this worksheet, you will write down items that you want. While your goals provide direction for your personal finances, wants are defined as things or activities that bring enjoyment but are not essential for daily living. Think through your daily and monthly purchases to identify wants. After listing them, think through which items on the list are most important and number them by priority. Don't worry about how much each item costs. Financial planning starts with goals and prioritization. You'll have plenty of time later to look over balances and costs.

List your wants in the 'Item' column. Use the 'Priority' column to number the items in order of importance. You can refer to the list of items on the next page for examples of wants.

Item	Priority

Examples of Wants

Beauty Salon / Hair Dresser

Cable/Satellite

Clothing

Club Memberships

Eating Out

Education/Lessons

Electronics

Entertainment

Gifts

Miscellaneous

Newspaper

Recreational Supplies

Streaming Television/Movies

Tithing/Charitable Giving

Homework

Homework for Session One is to consider what it is you want to get out of your financial therapy experience. As you think of items to add to your wants from the Wanted Financial Prioritization Worksheet, add them to your list.

Step Two: Need

Objectives
- ❖ Prioritize your current financial needs
- ❖ Identify differences between the WANTS and NEEDS priority lists
- ❖ Create a combined priority list that is a compromise of the WANTS and NEEDS lists
- ❖ Decide whether to continue or to cease therapy before collecting financial documents
- ❖ Identify heuristics regarding your personal finances

Step Two Rationale
Step Two (Sessions Two and Three) provides you with an opportunity to resolve any ambivalence you may have about being in therapy. You are encouraged to make your own decisions without undue influence by therapists. Activities in these sessions highlight differences between what you want versus what you need. The concept of heuristics is defined in these sessions and you are encouraged to identify your own heuristics.

Session Two

Materials Provided
- ❖ Contemplative Stage of Readiness Worksheet
- ❖ Financial Genograms Worksheet
- ❖ Needs Financial Priority Worksheet
- ❖ Combined Prioritization Worksheet

Purpose of Session Two
Session Two introduces you to the contemplative stage of readiness, and helps you understand the positive and negative impact of making financial changes. Financial genograms are used to analyze how finances were addressed in the family of origin. After prioritizing needs, you will consolidate wants and needs to produce a complete list of prioritized financial items.

Contemplative Stage of Readiness Worksheet

The best way to describe this stage is to say "I'm not sure." There are positive and negative sides in financial therapy. The positives are pretty obvious: get out of debt, eliminate creditors, happier family and so on. Sound good? What's there not to like? But the negatives are also obvious: budget, fewer impulse purchases, fewer vacations, fewer just about everything. Being in financial therapy takes a lot of work. Nothing about it is passive. Mostly, it's all about change. That's why it's not an easy decision. It's also not easy because just about everyone is pressuring you to get your finances in order. But it's probably not clear what that means. Get out of debt, eliminate creditors and so on? It's not going to happen overnight, and what about friends and family members who are expecting some results? Being in financial therapy is a serious decision.

Write your answers to the following questions in the space provided.

1. What makes me want to stick with financial therapy?

2. What makes me think that it's not going to work?

3. Who is going to support you in working towards your goals?

4. Who will make it more difficult to meet your goals?

These are the types of questions that will help you decide whether to stay in financial therapy or not.

Financial Genograms Worksheet

One way people learn financial habits is from examples of the way finances are managed by those close to them. Genograms have been used in many therapeutic settings to help clients understand how family dynamics have played a part in their lives.

A genogram is similar to a family tree in that you draw out members of your extended family. However, a genogram is also used to understand factors from your family that influence your life. In a financial genogram, symbols are used to represent financial behaviors or occurrences that have impacted your relationship with finances. Some symbols you might use are given in the table to the right. If there is not a symbol that you feel represents a financial situation you would like to show in your financial genogram, make up a symbol, or simply write next to the appropriate family member what that situation is. Refer to the following page to see examples of symbols and a completed genogram before completing your own.

Male	Female	Fused/Enmeshed
☐	◯	≡
Healthy	Financially Minded	Cutoff/Withdrawn
=	$	⊣⊢
Financial Infidelity	Addiction	Credit Misuse
∧∧∧	A	C
Hostile	Economic Hardship	Divorced
⋁⋁⋁⋁	E	—⫽—

Example genogram:

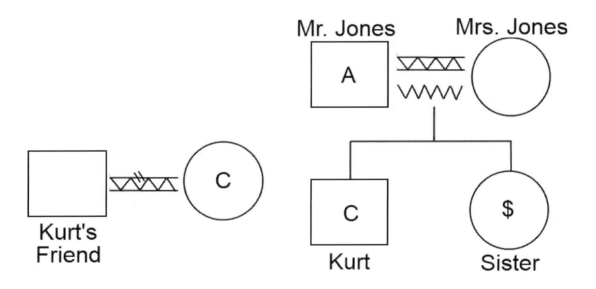

Draw out your own financial genogram here:

Families can play a large part in shaping your financial lifestyle. Whether through positive or negative influences, each relationship contributes to your spending habits or beliefs about money. The questions below will help you understand how your relationships affect your personal finances.

Write your answers to the following questions in the space provided.

1. What patterns do you see within your financial genogram?

2. What relationships stand out to you?

3. What relationships have most influenced your financial lifestyle?

Needs Financial Priority Worksheet

For this worksheet, don't worry about the cost of each item. Right now, only think through what you need and list the priority number you would give to that item. This may be really different from what you want. As you put down every item on the worksheet, think "Do I need this item/service to live?" "Would I not be able to go to school or work if I didn't have it?" Hint: Rent/mortgage probably goes near the top of your list. Okay, now go ahead and push yourself to only put down things that are really, really the basics.

List your needs in the 'Item' column. Use the 'Priority' column to number the items in order of importance. You can refer to the list of items on the next page for examples of needs.

Item	Priority

Examples of Needs

Car Insurance
Car Payment
Car Repairs
Cell Phone/Landline
Childcare
Credit Cards
Doctor/Dentist
Education
Gas
Groceries
Health Insurance

Household Items (e.g. Napkins, toilet paper)
Medicine/Prescriptions
Mortgage
Personal Loans
Pet food/Expenses
Rent
Retirement
Student Loans
Taxes
Utilities

Combined Prioritization Worksheet

At this point, go ahead and reconcile the two sets of priorities previously discussed. Consider what level of priority the item would have if you were to combine the priority level of want with the priority level of need. It requires going through item by item to see the best compromises between what is wanted and what is needed.

Use previously completed worksheets to copy your list of WANTS and NEEDS items and their corresponding priority number. Use the 'Combined Priority' column to number all of the items in order of importance.

Item	WANTS Priority	NEEDS Priority	COMBINED Priority

Homework
Continue thinking about your priorities as you go about your day-to-day activities.

Session Three

Materials Provided
- ❖ Your Personal Heuristics Worksheet
- ❖ Pause, Plan, and Purchase Worksheet
- ❖ Language of Money Worksheet

Purpose of Session Three
Examine the prioritized budget and discuss the heuristics, or meaning behind, the way the priorities were chosen. Personal heuristics are explained to help in future financial planning.

Your Personal Heuristics Worksheet

A heuristic is a belief, a rule of thumb, an intuitive judgment, and the "common sense" that people implement when they make financial decisions. For example, many people buy things on sale to "save money." The heuristic here is that "buying things on sale saves money." This can be true sometimes, but false other times. It's important to understand what motivates your decisions and answer questions such as "Do I really need the things now?" or "Do I really need the quantity I have to buy in order to get something on sale (think big box stores)," or "Do I really need to save money on brand names?" or "What are the differences for me between the store brand and the brand name products?"

There are underlying emotional reasons on why people spend money. Sometimes fear of embarrassment or past history can cause people to make financial decisions. For example, a person who never had new clothes as a child may find particular enjoyment in purchasing new clothes. Emotions can lead to problematic mental shortcuts that encourage people to be impulsive. Planning on what to buy sounds dreary, but it can also save lots of money.

Understanding your personal heuristics about finances and money are at the heart of financial therapy. The following questions will help you identify your own heuristics. Answer each one with the first thing that comes to mind. Don't overthink it because there are no right or wrong answers. This is about getting to know yourself.

Finish the following sentences by writing in the space provided.

1. I am encouraged to buy something when:

2. I think buying name brand items is:

3. Buying used items is:

4. Sometimes, I use money to:

5. I tend to spend more money when I feel:

6. Thinking of money and emotions together makes me think:

7. I always buy something when:

Looking at your answers to the questions above, think about what kind of heuristics might drive your spending habits. The questions below will help you further explore your heuristics.

8. What were your hidden heuristics (heuristics you never realized you had)?

9. How do you think these heuristics affect your financial behavior?

Pause, Plan, and Purchase Worksheet

The Pause/Plan/Purchase heuristic is a behavioral rule. It just means to Pause and Plan before making a Purchase. Credit and debit cards make it easy to spend money, even when you know you shouldn't. So, what will keep you from spending money you know you shouldn't? The key is to pause, plan, and then decide whether you really should make the purchase. If you can stop and think about what you're doing, then it'll give you a chance to plan on what to do next. Just slowing down for a moment gives you a chance to plan before you buy something. There are studies that suggest that any kind of delay before making a purchase decreases its desirability. It decreases impulsive behavior. At the very least, it provides a moment to reconsider the necessity and costs of the purchase. We all have heuristics that shape our financial habits, but using new behavioral rules creates new heuristics and allows us to examine our old ones.

Write your answers to the following questions in the space provided.

1. Write down one example when you were able to just slow down before you did anything.

2. What happened when you slowed down?

3. When did it happen?

4. Where were you when you slowed down before buying something?

5. What does it mean to you that you were able to slow down when you did?

The Three P's rule is essential when you are faced with the typical cues for making unwise purchases. The cues come from a person's surroundings. We tend to make unwise purchases in specific places and times, and with specific people, or for specific reasons. Now, of course, we can make unwise decisions at any time or place for any reason, but some cues make it much more likely to make mistakes.

In the space below, write down the cues that affect you and what will help you remember the Three P's rule.

1. When

2. Where

3. Who was around when it happened?

4. Why did you make the decision that you did?

Language of Money Worksheet

Making and using money is an emotional action. Just like saying words can create emotions, using money can also create emotions. Imagine the message given when a person hides money, has credit card problems, or loses a job. It is normal to have emotional reactions to purchases, items, and financial issues. What causes the most trouble is the way we talk about our emotional reactions to how money is saved or spent. Our heuristics regarding money shape our behaviors and directly affect our relationships. It becomes even more complicated when we already have a complex emotional relationship with a person with whom we share financial responsibility.

Write your answers to the following questions in the space provided.

1. When was the last time that you argued with someone about money?

2. What did it mean about your relationship with someone to have that emotional discussion about money?

3. How did the argument end?

4. What effect did it have on your relationship with the person, and with money?

Homework

Consider the heuristics you identified in the session and continue to list the heuristics that guide your financial behaviors. Use the Pause, Plan, Purchase heuristic while shopping and write down what happened as a result. Compile financial documents and bring them to the next session. Use the items in the Combined Prioritization Worksheet to guide your search for financial documents. There should be a bill, receipt, or statement for each item on your priority list.

Step Three: Have

Objectives

- ❖ Collect and compile all relevant financial documents
- ❖ Consider the benefits of making a financial lifestyle change
- ❖ Complete a budget worksheet that represents past financial behavior
- ❖ Organize the financial documents on a Financial Mirror to allow visual inspection

Step Three Rationale

Step Three (Sessions Four and Five) helps you find meaning in your compiled financial documents. Locating and examining financial documents will reveal dreaded truths. These revelations are critical in being able to go forward with responsible financial behaviors. The momentum created by finding and organizing financial documents solidifies advancement into the preparation stage of readiness.

Session Four

Materials Provided
- ❖ Preparation Stage of Readiness Worksheet
- ❖ Mapping the Financial Landscape Worksheet
- ❖ Challenge Question Worksheet

Purpose of Session Four
Session Four will help you prepare to make changes in your spending, and in the way you think about your finances, search for and/or locate financial documents and investigate the benefits of making a financial lifestyle change.

Preparation Stage of Readiness Worksheet

"Be prepared." The old adage of Boy Scouts means even more when you're preparing to change a financial lifestyle. The stakes are huge in changing a financial lifestyle and require a lot of thought. It seems reasonable to prepare yourself for the changes facing you. In financial therapy, the key to preparation is coming up with a budget that is perfect. Well, no budget is perfect, but it should be based on WANT/NEED priorities, consideration of heuristics, and the willingness to make changes. Although those considerations are central in creating a budget, there is one area that is of first importance: locating and compiling financial documents.

Financial documents can create the biggest crisis in a person's life. It may be the first time that you will actually see your financial identity. It may not be pretty. However, it is important in shedding light on murky personal finances. By locating most or all financial documents, you will see what your finances are and are not. For example, they may not be as bad as you thought, or you may think you spend far too much money in one area when it is actually another area. One way or another, you need to know what you owe or don't owe. After the initial shock, knowing what you spend in certain areas may become like a comfortable pair of shoes. They are initially stiff but become softer over time. The problem is that, in the beginning, the stiffness may be intolerable. With finances, the temptation is to "discard the shoes" before they have had time to become comfortable. On the other hand, there may be no choice.

Seeing all your documents is like opening Pandora's Box. Once opened, it's hard to continue to deny that there is a significant amount of personal debt or that a car is close to being repossessed. Preparation here is getting all the documents and the emotional readiness to make a budget in the next Step. It is the acknowledgement that a new financial lifestyle is imminent.

In preparing for change, it's important to get ready for change, but also not to catastrophize it. In short, it's important to know how much to prepare. On the following page, assess how much preparation is needed.

Write your answers to the following questions in the space provided.

1. What will I need to do to completely prepare to create a budget?

2. What do I need to do to emotionally prepare to create a budget?

3. What is the worst thing that could happen?

4. What is the best thing that could happen?

5. What will keep me from being prepared to create a budget and then change my financial lifestyle?

6. How will I celebrate in being ready to make a budget (without spending much money?)

Mapping the Financial Landscape Worksheet

A budget isn't much good without all the bills, invoices, statements, and receipts. That's the reason why you've got to find them all. Yes, all of them. They are carefully hidden away in drawers, boxes, online receipts, bedside tables, kitchen drawers, attics, under the furniture and. . . .and. . . .I can't imagine where you're going to find all of them. But you have to find all of them, or at least know for sure the balance of accounts or amount due.

You may wonder why you need to find them all. It seems like some sort of punishment, but it is important because all your statements, bills, receipts, and invoices tell a story of your financial life. Without knowing the entire story, it's hard to create a new one. After all, you wouldn't want a character from a past story ruining your new story. All those pieces of paper tell a story about relationships. For example, the credit card statement from February 2005 may create memories of a Valentine's Day. Or a plumber's bill brings back memories of the chaos in your house when the water heater broke down. All those memories are recorded in the pieces of paper. Not to have those pieces of paper may risk losing those memories. Don't do it; find your memories.

In the table below, use the 'Item' column to list all the bills or statements you may need to collect in order to have all of your financial information available. Then, write an "X" in either the 'Can't Find It' or 'Got It' column to indicate whether or not you have found the document/statement. Use the last two columns to list the balance and monthly payment/expense for applicable items. Refer to the list of possible items on the next page for examples of documents.

Item	Can't Find It	Got It	Balance	Monthly Expense

Write your answer to the following question in the space provided.

What kind of story does your Financial Landscape tell?

Examples of Financial Documents

Bank Statements

Car Insurance Documents

Car Loan Statements

Credit Card Statements

Loan Documents

Medical Bills

Monthly Membership Plan Statements

Payment Plans

Receipts

Utility Bill

Challenge Question Worksheet

Are you ready to change? Before you answer the question, it's important to really understand that it's your choice. People may tell you that it's in your best interest to change, but you have to ignore them for right now. The question is whether you're ready to change. Right now, right here, you can choose to go either way. Remember, what we're doing here is only one option. It is not the only option. The easiest thing is to agree that you should change and celebrate. But you haven't answered the question: are you ready to change? Is it your choice?

There is something called the "decisional balance." That's just a way of saying that there comes a point when you and only you have a choice on what direction to take. Don't be persuaded by any one person or idea. In the end, you'll have to go one way or the other. Today, you can choose to go ahead with this financial therapy or you can also do an honorable thing and say that it is not for you. Whichever way you choose, make sure that it's your choice.

Write your answers to the following questions in the space provided.

1. Who are the people who will most benefit from choices that you make today?

2. Who will benefit the least from the choices that you make today?

3. What will be the biggest change in your life from any choices you make today?

4. What will stay the same in your life from anything that you decide to do today?

5. What does it mean to make it your own choice and not one that someone else made for you?

Homework
Continue collecting and compiling financial documents. Use the Financial Landscape Worksheet as a guide for your search. If you can't find a document, make an estimate. Update your estimate when you can.

Session Five

Materials Provided
- ❖ Current Budget Worksheet
- ❖ The Financial Mirror Worksheet

Purpose of Session Five

Session Five consists of creating a budget that reflects current spending and creating a financial mirror. The financial mirror will reflect your financial "self," and will help you understand what changes you need to make.

Current Budget Worksheet

When completing the worksheet below, examine each item to ensure that it is an accurate approximation. Continue to consider the heuristics associated with past spending, and how those heuristics can be changed for future financial behaviors. The worksheet below will be a representation of your current budget and spending habits. Each individual has varying preferences on how to list items and categories. Some prefer more detailed budgets with each type of purchase being its own category. Others combine similar types of purchases or services into one category. Do what works best for you.

For each 'Item/Category' listed on this worksheet, list its 'Priority,' the 'Balance' if applicable (e.g. credit cards, car loan), and the amount of money you have been paying each month for this item in the 'Monthly Payment' column. Also, include the 'Heuristics' that explain why you purchase each item or why you spend that particular amount. Turn the page to see a list of examples of budget items and categories.

Item/Category	Priority	Balance	Monthly Payment	Heuristics

Examples of Budget Items

Beauty Salon

Cable/Satellite/Phone

Car Insurance

Car Payment

Car Repairs

Cell Phone

Childcare

Clothing

Club Memberships

Credit Cards

Doctor/Dentist

Eating Out

Education/Lessons

Entertainment

Gas

Gifts

Groceries

Health Insurance

Household Items (e.g. Napkins, toilet paper)

Medicine/Prescriptions

Miscellaneous

Mortgage

Newspaper

Personal Loans

Pet Food/Expenses

Rent

Retirement

Streaming Television/Movies

Student Loans

Taxes

Tithing

Utilities

The Financial Mirror Worksheet

Looking at yourself in the mirror after a long night can be a real shock. And looking at yourself in a fluorescent light anywhere is not a pleasant experience. A Financial Mirror is one of those fluorescent light situations. It shows every fault, every financial mistake that you've made. However, a Financial Mirror also shows the good things that you've done mixed in with the not-so-good purchases that you made. The point is that nothing is being hidden, whether good or bad, it's all there for the viewing.

This is the first step in really making a good financial decision. It's hard to know what to do until you know where you are. By creating a Financial Mirror, you are able to see it each week and see changes in it. The same thing is true with other mirrors; it shows where you are right now versus where you were last week or the week before.

The Financial Mirror is a "mirror" in which your financial self is reflected back to you. You can create your own financial mirror by putting all your financial documents onto cork or paper bulletin boards. The purpose of the Financial Mirror is to create a visual display of your income and expenses. This visual display allows an emotional understanding of your financial behavior.

The items collected for your Financial Landscape are used to create a visual display of how money is being spent. Organize the financial documents (e.g., credit card statements, bank statements) and using pushpins or tape, put your documents onto a corkboard or large piece of paper hung on a wall. This will act as your Financial Mirror. The documents may be organized on the board by whichever method you choose. Some individuals prefer to group them by budget categories or separate wants and needs.

Write your answers to the following questions in the space provided.

    1. When you look at your financial mirror, what stands out to you?

2. Are there any financial documents or spending habits that you see on the financial mirror that make you uncomfortable?

3. What would you change about your financial mirror if you could? What would you keep the same?

Homework
Continue to organize your financial documents. Reevaluate the current budget based on new information to ensure that it is accurate. Track expenditures so you have a realistic understanding of how you are spending money.

Step Four: Do

Objectives

- ❖ Compare income to expenses using the financial documents collected in earlier sessions
- ❖ Create a budget that matches income to expenses
- ❖ Demonstrate the use of a Blackline Budget Priorities Worksheet
- ❖ Demonstrate a routine to periodically review the budget created in these sessions

Step Four Rationale

Step Four (Session Six) is notable in matching income with expenses. To reach a balanced budget, you will be asked to create a budget within your means, and one that reflects your priorities. The budget created in Step Four provides the action plan for future financial behaviors.

Session Six

Materials Provided
- ❖ Action Stage of Readiness Worksheet
- ❖ Action Stage: "Go" Worksheet
- ❖ Creating and Using Budgets Handout
- ❖ Blackline Budget Priorities Worksheet
- ❖ Track it Now: Purchases Worksheet
- ❖ Track it Now: Budget Worksheet

Purpose of Session Six

Session Six helps you to understand the flexibility inherent in a budget, but also the limitations.

Action Stage of Readiness Worksheet

Change is difficult. As much as we would like change to happen without having to constantly monitor it, this is sadly not how the world works. When we make a change in our life, especially in an important area like our finances, it is difficult to act on changes we want to make. It can also be frightening. Many people do not make changes in their lives because they are afraid they will fail. To avoid failure, they avoid action. People who avoid acting simply because they are afraid to fail never gain the experience they need in order to successfully accomplish difficult tasks.

The action stage of change comes when you feel ready to try and apply the principles you have learned to your life. This consists of small steps to test the waters of change. Action is looking at your budget and planning ahead to spend according to your budget, and then following through with those plans.

There are two important things to remember about the action stage of readiness. First, failure is acceptable. People who make a change and stick to it without failing even once, are few and far between. We must accept that we will fail a few times. Acceptance of failure frees us to begin again without punishing ourselves for shortcomings that everyone experiences.

Second, the action stage of readiness is that not acting is as much of a choice as acting. If we ignore our budget, if we go over a spending limit or refuse to pay a bill, these are also choices. The following questions may help you in moving into the action stage of change.

Write your answers in the space provided.

1. What is your level of commitment to the changes you will be making?

2. What have you done to prepare yourself to make the changes you are focusing on?

3. If you are afraid your commitment level is low, but you still want to pursue these changes, how are you going to help yourself act?

4. Is there something that inspires you to make these changes?

5. Many times we need something in our lives to help us stay strong. What will be your source of strength when you fail (remembering that everyone does fail)?

Action Stage: "Go" Worksheet

"Not Sure, Ready, Get Set, and now it's Go." It is not surprising that this stage comes only after the first three stages have been traversed. In the metaphor used in the previous stage, it's now time to start the race. The first stages have been important in developing resolve and getting ready for a new financial lifestyle. You've found out where you were, but now it's time to create a new map or budget. Not surprisingly, a map to get through the next stage of change is essential. That map is a budget. The past is important because it shows how you allocated your income in the past. This stage is all about prioritizing, reprioritizing, and allocating your money.

Push comes to shove. Rubber hits the road. Fish or cut bait. We've heard all of them. In financial therapy, everything leads up to creating a budget and following it. By now, you've seen why budgets work and why they don't. Budgets are not a moralistic judgment; they are not a financial straitjacket. They are action plans that balance what you want with what you need situated within how much money you make. It's reasonable when you think about it. You can't spend more than you make without the bill coming due.

Think about the questions below and see whether your answers differ from what they were before you started financial therapy.

Consider the following statements and circle 'Yes' or 'No' to indicate if you agree. Write your answer why in the space provided.

Budgets are necessary.

YES   NO

Why?

Budgets are pretty much dollars and cents.

YES   NO

Why?

Budgets are more than anything a compromise.

YES   NO

Why?

Budgets represent a financial lifestyle.

YES   NO

Why?

Creating and Using Budgets Handout

It's important to understand how to get started talking about budgets. It's a matter of making everything balance. Your budget balances your wants and needs, your income and expenses, and your present and future financial lifestyle. Too much emphasis on wants in your budget and you won't have enough money for your needs. When you think about your budget, think about how to balance it. Remember, your budget must reflect you: your wants and needs, income and expenses, and present and future financial lifestyle.

Just like money has its own language, budgets also have a language. Well, actually, it's more of a story than a language. Each item on a budget represents some sort of story. Undoubtedly, your budget is an interesting story. It's silly, but think through what kind of plotline your budget would tell an audience. Take one of your budget sheets and make up a story on each line item. For example, "The cat is my friend. Maybe my only friend." Or, "The cable bill keeps me going. Without my cable shows, I think that I would go nuts." And so on. Each line item should bring with it a different story. Here's the kicker. When you have to reprioritize your budget, how will that affect your life story?

Blackline Budget Priorities Worksheet

In order to know on what you can spend money, you have to know a) how much money will be coming in, and b) where you can put that money once you have it. When you let money control you, the money tends to decide to go in whichever direction it pleases. Decide where the money will go, and then send it there! Making a Blackline Budget will help you send your money where it needs to go. At this point, you should have enough information in your WANTS and NEEDS prioritization worksheets, as well as information from your financial landscape, to begin to put together a prioritized budget.

The following steps will help you organize a new, prioritized budget:

1. In pencil, list the items on your budget from most important to least important. Use the Current Budget Worksheet as a guide.

2. Write the minimum payment and A.P.R. for credit card payments. Use the previously completed Current Budget Worksheet to list the current amount of money spent on each item/category each month.

3. Use the 'Planned Amount' column to list the amount of money you plan to spend on each budget item/ category per month.

4. Know the amount of money you will have (i.e. monthly income).

5. Starting with the first item, add together the dollar amounts from the 'Planned Amount' column. Once you reach the amount of money that you have available (i.e. monthly income), draw a black line under the last item. You cannot afford to spend money on anything under the black line.

6. You may have to reprioritize or adjust spending allotments in order for your budget to fit your needs.

7. Once finished making adjustments, use additional Budget Worksheets at the end of this workbook to list your final budget and to keep track of your spending.

Item/Category	Min. Payment / APR	Current Amount	Planned Amount

Now, if you have followed the above steps, the results can sometimes look rather bleak. Only having enough money for bills and half of the groceries you planned on buying can be depressing. However, understanding what you have money for and what you cannot afford gives you power. Remember that each item on your budget represents you sending your money out to work for you. Whether it is working for you to keep you in an apartment, to give food to your children, or to let you enjoy your Saturday afternoon, you are putting it to work. Your goal is to get as much "work" out of your money as you can, for as few dollars as possible. Your black line budget begins to be your friend when you are able to move around the amount of money you spend on certain items so that you can fit more of the things you want above that black line. For example, is your housing taking up too many dollar signs above the black line? You may want to consider finding a different place to live. Does the money you set aside to go out prevent you from putting a haircut in above the black line? Don't be afraid to move money around (where possible) in order to get as many things in above the black line that you need/want as possible. It may take some compromising on your part, but it will also help you know what you need to do in order to fulfill your needs.

Write your answer to the following question in the space provided.

What are some changes you will have to make today in order to start following this budget?

Homework

Implement the changes discussed when creating your budget and track your spending to see if it is in line with your new budget. Use the following worksheets to track your spending during the next couple weeks. The first worksheet will help you track your spending and the second will help to see if your spending is in line with your new budget.

Track It Now: Purchases

1. List budget categories for which the totals change based on purchases for wants or needs. Some examples may be food, personal care, or clothing. You can list up to five categories.
2. Use the boxes below each item to list purchases. Saving receipts will help you with tracking purchases.
3. Add together the purchases from the row to find the purchase total.

Item 1	Item 2	Item 3	Item 4	Item 5
Total	Total	Total	Total	Total

Track It Now: Budget

1. *Using the categories from the previous worksheet, list them below in the first column.*
2. *Use the Blackline Budget Worksheet to write the planned budget total for each item.*
3. *Use the previous Track It Now: Purchases worksheet to list the purchase totals.*
4. *Subtract the purchase total from the budget total to find the difference. A positive difference means you have spent less than you planned, a negative difference means you have gone over budget.*

Item/Category	Budget Total	− Purchase Total	= Difference
Example: Food	$200	$195	$5

Step Five: Plan

Objectives

- ❖ Create a financial plan that addresses budgeting, debt elimination, and asset accumulation
- ❖ Re-examine current budget expenditures as a reflection of previously established priorities
- ❖ Adopt strategies to cope with financial downturns
- ❖ Adopt strategies to adhere to budgetary priorities when faced with various financial situations

Step Five Rationale

Step Five (Sessions Seven and Eight) provides materials and exercises for you that will help you maintain the behavioral changes you have made during financial therapy. It also provides opportunities for you to return to healthy financial behaviors after encountering roadblocks, and to learn how to handle difficult financial situations, such as debt, money and family, and the dangers of financial success.

Session Seven

Materials Provided
- ❖ Maintenance Level of Readiness Worksheet
- ❖ Small Picture Worksheet
- ❖ Getting Back on Track Worksheet
- ❖ "I Deserve Something" Handout
- ❖ Money for Loved Ones Worksheet
- ❖ Debt Elimination Calendar Worksheet
- ❖ Promises and Budgets Handout
- ❖ Financial Dangers of Success Handout

Purpose of Session Seven
The purpose of Session Seven is to help you understand how to carry on with your new financial understanding, and how to recover when missteps occur.

Maintenance Stage of Readiness Worksheet

Sometimes, congratulations just aren't enough. The problem with success is that it's hard to keep it going. The term, "maintenance" says it all: maintain change. It's not surprising that the maintenance stage comes after the action stage. After all, the action stage is the end result of a buildup to get ready for a change. Unfortunately, change at one point doesn't mean that it will continue.

With financial therapy, building a budget and establishing a new financial lifestyle is a culmination of efforts, but it is also the beginning. Living by a budget is like living on a diet. It's really good for you, but it doesn't mean that it's a lot of fun. In fact, a good financial lifestyle doesn't mean that you are "living the good life."

There is a saying among alcoholics, "One day at a time." The same can be said for people who are living on a budget. It's important to live one day at a time . . . but within a long-term budget. Sometimes, a budget is much easier if you don't think about tomorrow. Answer the questions below and see how you will be able to maintain a financially smart lifestyle.

Write your answers to the following questions in the space provided.

1. What will help you keep within your budget?

2. What accomplishments will make you proud to keep up your efforts?

3. What accomplishments will be hard to maintain?

Small Picture Worksheet

By now, the big picture is probably getting clear. Make a budget, live within your means, and keep track of what you're spending. Keeping track of what you are spending is what we call "the small picture". What were your good purchases this week? What were your bad purchases? Remember, the good ones were those in your budget, and ones that fit your priorities. The bad ones were impulsive purchases, and nowhere to be found in your budget or priorities. More important than the purchases, good or bad, was why you made them. In the Small Picture Worksheet, write down the good and bad purchases and put the heuristic next to the item.

List items or services purchased in the first column. For each item, write the cost or balance and describe the heuristic for purchasing each item.

Good or Bad Item/Service	Cost/ Balance	Heuristic

Getting Back on Track Worksheet

Budgets and diets have a lot in common; it's easy to fall off the wagon. And that's the rub. It's easy to get discouraged and quit your budget or diet when you can't maintain the standards that you set for yourself. The more pressure that you place on yourself, the more discouraged that you'll feel when you do fall off the wagon. Here are some ideas to remember. It's important to do everything that can be done to stay within your budget. When you do exceed your budget, take the following steps.

1. Assess changes in spending strategy by looking at which line items should be changed.
2. Assess whether the mistake was a one-time or a continuous event.
3. No self-recrimination on not following the budget.
4. Consider changing the budget (i.e., reprioritizing the budget) to ensure that you'll be able to stick with it.
5. Examine alternate heuristics to increase mindful financial behaviors (i.e., Pause/Plan/Purchase)

Consider the following questions in order to get back on track and write your answers in the space provided.

1. When will you be most at risk in not keeping to your budget?

2. What strategies will you use to avoid temptation?

3. What will you change if you don't stay within your budget on one occasion?

4. What will you change about your budget if you don't stay within your budget on several occasions?

"I Deserve Something" Handout

One common problem in the maintenance stage of Step Five is that you can experience a sense of deprivation. Following a budget is much like being on a diet. After following the budget/diet for a period of time, the initial euphoria of being disciplined wanes. Comments such as "I deserve something" that results from faithful adherence to the budget suggest that you are about to make an unwise or at least unplanned purchase.

The effects of unplanned purchases are both budgetary and emotional. The budgetary fall-out is deciding which expense has been put aside in light of the new, unplanned purchase. The emotional fall-out is more serious. After a new financial lifestyle has been adopted, this setback may encourage a reversion to previous spending habits. In short, guilt reduces self-confidence and planful behavior.

Planning for the "I deserve something" phenomena consists of telling yourself that feeling this feeling is normal and that it is common among people who have adopted a new lifestyle. In short, the deviation from the budget should be used as an opportunity to celebrate what has been accomplished.

Unexpected income or expenses can pose financial crises. Unexpected income can promote a sense of "free money" that encourages impulsive purchases; unplanned expenses may put a significant strain on a carefully constructed budget. The solution is to put into place an action plan that accommodates unexpected financial events. It may prove helpful to create a new heuristic on the meaning of unexpected financial events. How about the heuristic: "Unexpected income or feelings that "I deserve something" give me an opportunity to be flexible and to refine my budget."

Write your answers to the following questions in the space provided.

1. How will you reward yourself for sticking to your budget without breaking it?

2. What is your action plan for unexpected income? For unexpected expenses?

Money for Loved Ones Worksheet

Because money is just another name for emotional connections, it's important to be clear on its meaning among family members. Business relationships among family members are risky; loaning money is even more risky. There are real dangers for hurt feelings.

On the scale from 1 to 10 (1 being least likely, 10 being most likely), rate how likely each of the following events are.

1. What kinds of gifts or loans are you most likely to give?

    A Christmas gift_____

    An unplanned gift_____

    A loan_____

Write your answers to the following questions in the space provided.

2. What will you say when you are not able to give the Christmas gifts that your family members want?

3. What will you say when your family members or friends plead with you for a loan or a gift?

4. What will you do when they show that you have hurt their feelings?

78

5. How will you tell your family members about your new budget and what that means in terms of gifts and loans?

6. What is your current balance of loans and gifts to your family members?

7. What is the heuristic that keeps the balance from getting larger or smaller?

8. Rate how likely you are to explain your new budget and financial lifestyle to your family members?

Debt Elimination Calendar Worksheet

Credit card debt is completely bad. There are no tax benefits (unlike mortgages and student loans), the interest rates can go up to 30% APR and the relatively low repayments only serve to hide the enormity of debt. One goal of using a budget will be to help you eliminate debt. One way to help you understand and eventually eliminate your debt is to use a debt elimination calendar. In a debt elimination calendar you list the amount of all of your debts and the amount you pay for each debt every month. Then, after one debt is paid off, you move the money used for the first debt to help pay off the next debt on your calendar. Below is an example of a Debt Elimination Worksheet.

	Dentist	Credit Card	Auto Loan
Total Amount Due:	200	920	3400
January	50	110	250
February	50	110	250
March	50	110	250
April	50	110	250
May		(110+50) 160	250
June		160	250
July		160	250
August			(160+250) 410
September			410
October			410
November			410
December			10 (Final Payment)

The following is a blank Debt Elimination Calendar for your own use. Create your own debt elimination calendar, adding as many columns as you need to account for all debts. Don't forget, in loans and credit cards there is an interest rate that needs to be accounted. You may want to go online and search for an "interest rate calculator" in order to determine how long it will actually take to pay off your loan/debt. Bankrate.com has a credit card calculator that may be useful.

Total Amount Due:			
January			
February			
March			
April			
May			
June			
July			
August			
September			
October			
November			
December			

Promises and Budgets Handout

A budget is like a promise to yourself. But promises can be broken and so can budgets. Breaking a promise is all too human and is not surprising. What to do about broken promises is both simple and complex. First, the simple part. The manual has given you ideas on what to do when a budget doesn't seem to be working: find out where it's not working, figure out why it's not working and create a new budget. Simple, right? But what's the fallout for a broken promise? Trust goes down, right? Same thing with a broken budget: trust goes down. What should be done when the trust is a little bit lower? OK, here's the game plan.

1. Acknowledge that the budget hasn't worked. Just that. The budget hasn't worked. It doesn't matter why.

2. Commit yourself to action. This is a really hard thing to do. You may feel discouraged, puzzled, upset, and/or frustrated. The choices are hard ones: commit yourself to action or risk becoming helpless and paralyzed by a broken budget.

3. Determine the heuristic that allowed you to break your budget.

4. Create a new heuristic or modify the old one: give yourself a reason to create a new budget.

5. Create a new budget that incorporates the new heuristic (i.e., a reason for the new budget to be effective).

Sound confusing? Here's the summary: modify your old budget and fix whatever allowed you to break your budget. That's it. Really.

Financial Dangers of Success Handout

Chances are that you'll eventually earn more money. That's the good side. The other side is that it won't help matters much. More money doesn't always solve financial problems. For many people, having more money means that more money will be spent. And it is all too easy to spend more money than what is coming in. In fact, making more money may make a person wealthy, and then they stop caring about how much money is being spent. Of course, staying ignorant of your bank balance is hardly bliss! Just imagine making much more money, spending it, and becoming that much more in debt.

Financial dangers of success include job promotions, new jobs, becoming a two-job family, receiving an inheritance, prizes or any windfall. To understand the options, first consider what heuristic that you'll use to determine what will be done with the extra money. Here are some possibilities:

1. Save for a rainy day (because it might rain).
2. Go on a nice vacation (because it might never happen again).
3. Pay off debts (short term pain, long term gain).
4. Save money (never know when you might need it, including future expenses, like school, mortgage payments, and preparing for future pitfalls like job loss).
5. Give money to relatives (they may ask for it).
6. Give money to not-for-profit organizations, like a church.
7. Buy equities and bonds (spend money to make money).

As the number of options multiply, a careful examination of the heuristics is necessary. Of course, one option is to allocate money to different options much like a budget of newfound money. But whatever option is chosen, it is important to know why you are choosing it above the rest. Be honest: admit the heuristic that you're using and why it makes the most sense to you.

If you were given a gift of $1000, what would you do with it?

Homework
Create a plan for getting back on track after you've fallen away from using your budgeting plan. Complete the Debt Elimination Calendar Worksheet using your own debt information.

Session Eight

Materials Provided

- ❖ All About Future Priorities Handout
- ❖ All About Future Priorities Worksheet
- ❖ Banks and Credit Unions Handout
- ❖ Banks and Credit Union Handout and Worksheet
- ❖ Savings Accounts Handout
- ❖ Insurance Companies Handout
- ❖ Defining a Financial Plan Worksheet

Purpose of Session Eight

Session Eight is comprised of financial management strategies you may find useful when trying to overcome financial stressors. It also provides methods to use products and services from traditional personal finance organizations.

All About Future Priorities Handout

Priorities? A couple months ago, we started by talking about priorities. It seems right that we end here by talking about them. The same questions still exist here. "What do I really want?" and "What do I really need?" It'll take planning to get to what you want and need. This handout is all about where to store money. Where you store money will help you plan on how to spend it.

I think that it's hard to believe that people will want to sell you ways to store money and claim that they have solved your problems! It's not easy to talk to people who say that they want to help you but really want to sell you something that you may or may not need. You need some of what they have but it comes at a cost. We are going to say over and over again that there is nothing free in banks, credit unions, and insurance companies. There are hidden fees and costs just about everywhere you look. Still, it's time to get going. The best way to understand on what you have to do is to list who you're doing to visit.

- ❖ Banks
- ❖ Credit Unions
- ❖ Insurance Companies

You're buying products and services from each company. They are different in what they sell and how much it costs. They all say that they want to help and they usually are telling the truth. However, the bottom line is that they have to make a profit at your expense. Even when they tell the costs of their products and services, they may do so quickly. Here are some products that they sell:

- ❖ Checking Account
- ❖ Savings Account
- ❖ Certificates of Deposit
- ❖ Individual Retirement Accounts
- ❖ Mortgages
- ❖ Health Insurance
- ❖ Life Insurance
- ❖ Auto Insurance

The list goes on and on. These products are not free. These companies make profit by charging you fees and interest payments. The bottom line is that banks, credit unions, and insurance companies are profit-seeking companies that try to sell you things that you need and don't need.

All About Future Priorities Worksheet

This worksheet will help you review your most important wants and needs. Then, you will be able to see these important priorities represented as a dollar amount. To complete the worksheet below you may need to review some previously completed worksheets, such as the Combined Prioritization Worksheet and the Blackline Budget Priorities Worksheet.

Write your answers to the following questions in the space provided.

1) Name and prioritize your top three current wants.

     1)

     2)

     3)

2) Name and prioritize your top three current needs.

     1)

     2)

     3)

3) How much money will you need to obtain your three wants and needs?

4) Where will you keep the money that you need to obtain your wants and needs?

5) How will you keep track of how much money you have?

6) How will you prevent from losing everything that you have and want?

These questions are those that you'll need to answer to establish your financial priorities.

Banks and Credit Unions Handout

Let's be honest! Opening a checking account can be frustrating. You'd like to store some of your money in a safe place. You'd like to get started in setting a good financial lifestyle. So, what's the problem? Well, there are a whole lot of problems. It's always unclear on what banks do besides store people's money. They do charge a lot of fees on what they do for people. For example, they charge you a fee for you to store your money in a bank. They charge you a fee when you overdraw your checking account. They charge you a fee when you use an ATM machine. They charge you to get checks to access your money. In short, they make a lot of money by charging you fees. And they also make money by getting interest on the money that you store there.

So, why use banks anyway? It's because it is the first step in living out your new financial lifestyle. Well, maybe not the first step since you've already established priorities and set up a budget. But it shows you've accomplished a lot when you have a checking account. It's a success story. As you probably can guess, some good things in life aren't free and this is one of them. However, if you carefully consider your options before making decisions, you will be able to save a lot of money.

Here is what you should do:

1) Go to a credit union if possible; they have fewer fees and are a whole lot nicer.
2) Stick with a basic checking account. You should be able to open and maintain the account without being charged any fees.
3) Bring a friend for moral support when you go to open an account. Don't do it alone.
4) Build friendly relationships with your bankers.

Banks and Credit Unions Worksheet

There are a number of items that you will need to take with you when going to open a checking account. There are also certain questions you will want to know the answer to before deciding to open an account. Sometimes it helps to visit a few different credit unions or banks to find one that offers an account that is right for you. Use the list below to keep track of the items you need to bring and compare financial institutions. Remember to bring along a friend who already has a checking account.

Collect the following items (check box when item is collected):

1) Driver's License with your current address on it ☐
2) Any evidence of where you live, like a utility bill. ☐
3) Must be 18 years of age ☐
4) Must know Social Security Number. ☐

Ask the Following:	Bank #1	Bank #2	Bank #3
1) What is the monthly fee for maintaining this account?	$_____	$_____	$_____
2) What is the minimum balance for this account?	$_____	$_____	$_____
3) What is the fee for going under the minimum balance?	$_____	$_____	$_____
4) What interest do I earn on money in the account?	____%	____%	____%
5) Is the account for which I'm applying FDIC insured?	_____	_____	_____
6) What is the limit to the number of monthly transactions? (deposits/withdrawals, check writing, ATM uses)	_____	_____	_____
7) What is the fee for going over the number of transactions allowed?	$_____	$_____	$_____
8) Where can I withdraw cash without paying any fees?	_____	_____	_____
9) What is the fee for using an ATM machine that doesn't belong to this bank?	$_____	$_____	$_____

90

Savings Accounts Handout

What's the purpose of saving money when you don't have enough of it? That's the real problem with saving money: there just isn't enough of it when you need it. But sometimes you need money more than other times. Only you can decide when it's best to use money that you have set aside. One thing is clear: it is important to save money. The second most important thing: start saving now.

The fact is that your savings account balance will go up and down. That's just reality. What can start today is that you start saving. Don't worry about how much you save. All that matters is that you start saving today and keep on doing so on a regular basis. If it's not clear on how to save money, go back to your list of combined priorities. It's just a matter on how high up you place savings as a priority. Once it's set down as a priority, place it in your Blackline budget. And once you start, don't stop. That's it.

Here are some good questions to ask yourself:

1) How does financial insecurity affect your daily life? Saving money is a statement that you don't like financial uncertainty.

2) What does a successful savings account mean to you? Saving money is like staying on a budget; it makes people feel good about themselves.

3) What things will happen to make savings a more important priority? Prioritizing savings is akin to prioritizing any budget item; it's all a matter of priorities.

Insurance Companies Handout

Insurance companies like to make money. You'd like to have some spare money. That's the continual war that occurs. Do you like to gamble? A lot? Insurance companies exist to lower people's anxiety about death, accidents, and injuries. There are many different types of insurance companies and plans. Some are more expensive than others. The topic of insurance is complex and way beyond what can be discussed here. Before you invite an insurance agent to sell you insurance, be sure that you have done your homework. Let's start with car insurance. You're required to have liability car insurance (i.e., insurance policies that will pay the other guy when you're in an accident). The goal of insurance salespeople is to sell you policies for as much money as you'll need to pay the other guy in an accident. That means paying for his or her car repairs, injuries, and so on. Basically, liability insurance pays for damage and injuries that you've caused. Other kinds of car insurance basically pay for damages done to your own property. So, the moral of this story is that you are required to have liability insurance to drive a car (think of it as a driver's license) and so it's a NEED and not a WANT. The other moral is to avoid having accidents.

The second type of insurance policy is health insurance. If you thought that car insurance was complex, it pales by comparison to health insurance. Let me put it this way: people will take jobs not for how much they pay but whether the benefits include health insurance. There's no point in talking about health insurance since it requires a book in itself. Basically, what is important to consider is whether to have "catastrophic" health insurance. Catastrophic insurance pays for really big medical expenses but not the ordinary expenses. Here are some questions you might want to consider when thinking about insurance:

1) What does having medical insurance mean to you? Life insurance? Auto insurance?

2) What types of insurance do you already have? What types would you like to have?

3) Where do the different types of insurance fit into your combined priority list?

Defining a Financial Plan Worksheet

The following questions may help you look to the future in maintaining the changes you have made during financial therapy:

Write your answers to the following questions in the space provided.

1) What changes need to happen with your checking or savings accounts?

2) What is the first thing you will do to make the above changes happen?

3) Now that financial therapy is over, what is your financial goal?

4) What do you want your financial life to look like in five years?

5) After leaving here today, what three steps will you take to reach your goals?

    a. Step #1 and Date of Completion

    b. Step #2 and Date of Completion

    c. Step #3 and Date of Completion

Additional Worksheets

Budget Worksheet

Month: _____

Item/Category	Min. Payment / APR	Planned Amount	Amount Spent

Track It Now: Purchases

1. *List budget categories for which the totals change based on purchases for wants or needs. Some examples may be food, personal care, or clothing. You can list up to five categories.*
2. *Use the boxes below each item to list purchases. Saving receipts will help you with tracking purchases.*
3. *Add together the purchases from the row to find the purchase total.*

Item 1	Item 2	Item 3	Item 4	Item 5
Total	Total	Total	Total	Total

Track It Now: Budget

1. *Using the categories from the previous worksheet, list them below in the first column.*
2. *Use the Blackline Budget Worksheet to write the planned budget total for each item.*
3. *Use the previous Track It Now: Purchases worksheet to list the purchase totals.*
4. *Subtract the purchase total from the budget total to find the difference. A positive difference means you have spent less than you planned, a negative difference means you have gone over budget.*

Item/Category	Budget Total —	Purchase Total	= Difference
Example: Food	$200	$195	$5

Budget Worksheet

Month: _____

Item/Category	Min. Payment / APR	Planned Amount	Amount Spent

Track It Now: Purchases

4. *List budget categories for which the totals change based on purchases for wants or needs. Some examples may be food, personal care, or clothing. You can list up to five categories.*
5. *Use the boxes below each item to list purchases. Saving receipts will help you with tracking purchases.*
6. *Add together the purchases from the row to find the purchase total.*

Item 1	Item 2	Item 3	Item 4	Item 5
Total	Total	Total	Total	Total

Track It Now: Budget

5. Using the categories from the previous worksheet, list them below in the first column.
6. Use the Blackline Budget Worksheet to write the planned budget total for each item.
7. Use the previous Track It Now: Purchases worksheet to list the purchase totals.
8. Subtract the purchase total from the budget total to find the difference. A positive difference means you have spent less than you planned, a negative difference means you have gone over budget.

Item/Category	Budget Total	− Purchase Total	= Difference
Example: Food	$200	$195	$5

Notes

Notes

Notes

Made in the USA
Lexington, KY
26 February 2015